Checkup

by Miriam Sklar

ISBN: 978-1-338-75073-7
Illustrated by John Lund

Published by Scholastic Inc., 557 Broadway, New York, NY 10012

10 9 8 7 6 5 4 68 25 26 27/0

Printed in Jiaxing, China. First printing, January 2021.

Check my eyes.

Check my nose.

Check my ears.

Check my throat.

Check my back.

Check my heart.

Check every part!